Disney's Winnie the Pooh and the Windy Day

GROLIER BOOKS

It was a very windy day in the Hundred-Acre Wood. Pooh was sitting in his Thoughtful Spot.

All of a sudden the earth in front of him began to move.

"What could it be?" Pooh thought.

Gopher's head popped up.

"Oh, hello, Gopher," Pooh said.

"You should hurry home, Pooh," Gopher said very seriously. "It's going to be a very windy day."

"I don't mind," said Pooh. "I think I will go see my friends to wish them a very happy windy day."

So Pooh started off.

On his way Pooh met Piglet, who seemed to be in a great hurry!

"Where are you going?" Pooh called out to his friend.

"T-to tell you the truth," Piglet said, "I really don't know. I'm waiting for the wind to show me." At that very moment, Piglet was being swept away by the wind.

"Here," said Pooh.
"I'll help you."

Pooh took hold of
Piglet's scarf. But the
wind was very strong.
It lifted Piglet right off
the ground.

"Don't worry,
little Piglet," said
Pooh. "I've got you."

But the scarf began to unravel. Piglet started to fly
higher into the air.

Pooh held tightly to the string of wool. But the wind pulled Piglet along. Pooh followed him on the ground.

They came to Kanga's house.

Roo yelled, "Look! It's a kite. Can I fly it, Pooh!? Pleeease!"

"No, I'm sorry, Roo," Pooh called back. "But have a nice windy day!"

Eeyore had just finished
building a new house.
"That's it," Eeyore
said. "It'll stand for
a long time."

But just then, Pooh came by at full speed. He
crashed into Eeyore's new house. The sticks flew in
all directions.
"Oops. Sorry, Eeyore," cried
Pooh. "But have a nice
windy day!"
"Don't mention
it, Pooh,"
Eeyore said.

Rabbit was picking carrots in his garden. He loved carrots more than anything. But he wished there was a faster way to pull them up from the ground.

Suddenly, Rabbit heard a voice calling out to him.

"Have a nice windy day, Rabbit!" Pooh yelled, as the wind dragged him through Rabbit's carrot patch. Pooh's feet dug up the carrots. The carrots flew right into the wheelbarrow.

Rabbit was so happy! "Come back when I am ready to harvest my cabbage!" he called after Pooh.

At Owl's house, Owl was fast asleep.

Suddenly, the wind became very strong. Both Pooh and Piglet were lifted into the air.

Owl woke up because he heard a strange sound at the window. He wondered what it could be.

"Will you look at that!" Owl exclaimed. "Somebody has stuck Piglet and Pooh to my window."

Owl opened the window for them. Pooh and Piglet
flew right across the room and hit the wall.

"Correct me if I'm wrong," Owl began, "but isn't it quite windy today?"

"Y-yes, it's a very, very windy day," Piglet said, as he slid down onto a stool.

"Ooof!" Pooh said, landing in a chair. "Have a nice windy day, by the way."

"Thank you, Pooh," Owl said. "You know, that reminds me of a really windy day back in . . ."

"Excuse me, Owl," Pooh interrupted. "By any chance, would there be honey in that pot?" Pooh had noticed a pot sitting on Owl's table.

"Why, yes, of course," Owl said. "Help yourself."

But just as Pooh reached for the honey pot, Owl's house began to shake.

Pooh saved the honey pot from falling.

As Pooh started to eat the honey, the wind pushed over the tree. Poor Piglet flew across the room straight into Pooh. The honey smeared all over Pooh's face!

Owl's house crashed to the ground. Nobody was hurt. But Owl was a little confused.

"Somebody has tipped over my tree with my house in it," Owl said sadly. "It wasn't you, was it, Pooh?" Owl asked.

"I don't think so," was all Pooh could say.

Later, the windy day turned into a windy night. Pooh was at home in his bed when he heard a strange sound.

"Is that you, Piglet?" Pooh called out, after opening the front door. But there was no answer.

Suddenly, Tigger bounced in and pushed Pooh to the floor.

"Oh, you scared me," said Pooh.

"Yep!" Tigger said confidently. "Tiggers are wunnerful at being scary. But heffalumps and woozles are even more scary. They eat honey, you know! So you better beware!" Then, Tigger bounced out the door.

Pooh decided to stay up all night to protect his honey.

Pooh tried to stay
awake, but his eyelids
got very heavy.
Finally, he fell
asleep.

While asleep, Pooh had a terrible nightmare.
Heffalumps and woozles were everywhere.
They came in every shape and color. They were
stealing and eating his honey. Poor Pooh didn't
have a chance. His honey was being eaten right in
front of him.

Then Pooh
woke up, and he
discovered that his
house was flooded!

While Pooh was sleeping, it had started to rain in the Hundred-Acre Wood.

It had rained and rained and rained. The entire wood was flooded. It was a terrible night.

By the next morning, the water reached to the top of Piglet's door!

Inside, Piglet's house was also flooded. Piglet woke up because his bed started to float. He saw all his things floating around in the room.

"Oh, what am I going to do?" he asked himself. "I'm just a small animal that gets frightened very easily. What am I going to do?"

Piglet decided to do
something. He jumped on a
chair and paddled over to his
cupboard. On his way he
filled a few pots and pans
with some of the water.

He took a
piece of paper
and wrote a note.
Then, Piglet put
the note into a
bottle and threw
the bottle
out the
window. He
wanted someone to
come rescue him.

Finally, the water got so high that Piglet sailed out the window on his chair.

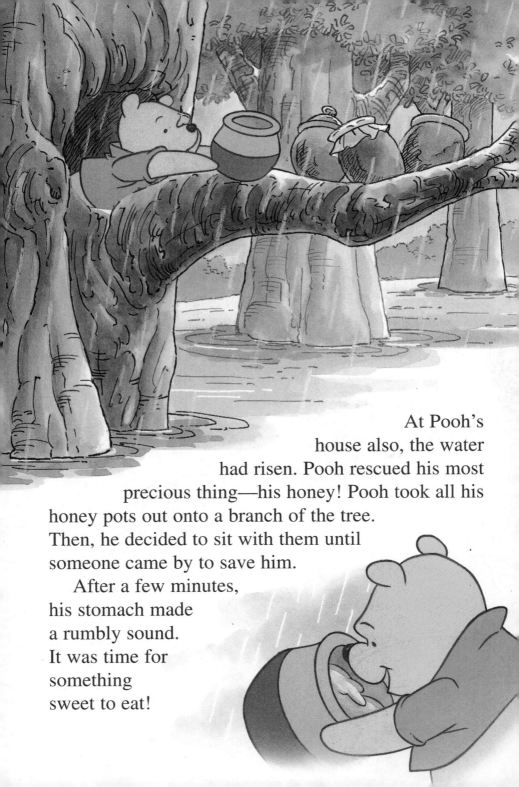

At Pooh's
house also, the water
had risen. Pooh rescued his most
precious thing—his honey! Pooh took all his
honey pots out onto a branch of the tree.
Then, he decided to sit with them until
someone came by to save him.

After a few minutes,
his stomach made
a rumbly sound.
It was time for
something
sweet to eat!

"Perhaps I should wait," Pooh said to himself.

"But I can't argue with an empty stomach! I'll just have a smackerel."

Pooh put his head in the pot and began to eat. All of a sudden, Pooh lost his balance and fell headfirst off the branch! Then, he floated down the river.

By now the rain had stopped. Everyone in the Hundred-Acre Wood went to Christopher Robin's house.

"Where are Piglet and Pooh?" Christopher Robin asked.

No one knew!

"Look what I've found!" cried Roo.

"Oh, it's a message in a bottle," Christopher Robin said. "How exciting! Here, I'll read it."

Chrisopher Robin took out the paper and read Piglet's note: "Help! Piglet (Me)."

"We have to go help Piglet," Christopher Robin said. "Owl, you must fly out and find Piglet!"

Owl flew over the Hundred-Acre Wood to look for Piglet. After a little while, he saw Piglet sailing along on his chair. Pooh was floating upside-down next to him. Owl told them a rescue team was on its way.

"I'm sorry, Owl," Piglet said. "B-but could you stay with me? This is very scary for such a small animal."

Owl tried to help Piglet by telling him a long story. Owl got so caught up in his story that he didn't hear Piglet suddenly cry out, "T-there's a waterwall— a waterfall up ahead! Owl, what are we going to do?"

Pooh and Piglet tumbled down the waterfall. Pooh came up sitting on Piglet's chair.

"There he is!" Christopher Robin yelled when he saw Pooh.

"Oh, hello, Christopher Robin," Pooh said. "Have you seen Piglet?"

Just then, Pooh's
honey pot came up from the
water. Christopher Robin
picked it up and out popped Piglet.
"Here I am!" Piglet cheered.
"Pooh, you have saved Piglet!"
Christopher Robin exclaimed.
"That was a very brave thing
to do."
"I have?" Pooh asked.
"Yes," said Christopher
Robin. "You deserve
a hero's party!"

Later that day, the friends had a party.

"We are having this party," Christopher Robin said, "because Pooh has done a very brave thing."

"Sorry to interrupt," Eeyore said suddenly, "but I've found it!"

"Found what?" they all wanted to know.

"A new house for Owl," Eeyore said.

Since Owl's house had fallen to the ground, Eeyore had been looking for a new house for Owl.

"Where is it?" Piglet wanted to know.
"Just follow me," Eeyore said.

Eeyore stopped outside Piglet's house.
"Why are we stopping here?"
Rabbit asked.
"It's Owl's new house," Eeyore
said happily.
"Yes. It says 'Owl's House' on
the sign," Owl said. "Even though
there are a few letters missing."
No one had the heart to
tell Eeyore that he was giving
away Piglet's house.

"What am I going to do?" Piglet said.
"Tell him it's your house," Rabbit said to Piglet.
"No," Piglet said sadly. "The house now belongs to our good friend Owl."

"But where are you going to live?" Kanga asked.

"He's going to live with me," Pooh said.

"Oh, thank you, Pooh!" Piglet said. "I would love that."

Everyone thought it was especially nice of Piglet to give his house to Owl. Also, they thought it was very heroic because Piglet loved his house more than anything in the world. So the party for Pooh was turned into a party for two heroes, Pooh and Piglet. Everybody sang and played all day.